Fit &

 **Fashionable** 

800 Coco Drive, Coconut Grove, FL 33133

DESCRIPTION OF THE COMPANY

Fit & Fashionable is mainly a wholesaler of fitness equipment and apparel, strategically located in Coconut Grove, FL. The clientele of Fit & Fashionable consists primarily of local gyms, wellness centers, retail outlets of sports equipment and apparel, and the general public. Fit & Fashionable is owned and operated by Marty Chavez.

You are employed to maintain the accounts and prepare financial statements for Fit & Fashionable. This practice set includes the transactions completed during April, which are intended to illustrate general principles of accounting rather than the techniques of the accounting system of a particular business. You are to analyze, record, and post these transactions for April. You will then journalize entries for accounts requiring adjustment, prepare month-end financial reports, and complete the closing process.

The information below contains a description of the contents of the practice set and instructions for completing the project manually. The practice set can also be completed utilizing the Cengage Learning General Ledger software, which is available online at CengageNOW.com. Instructions for using this general ledger software are provided on pages 3–5.

BOOKS OF ACCOUNT

Journals

The following journals are included in this booklet:

1. General Journal
2. Revenue Journal (also called a Sales Journal)
3. Purchases Journal
4. Cash Receipts Journal
5. Cash Payments Journal

Ledgers

The following ledgers are included in Booklet 2:

1. General Ledger
2. Accounts Receivable Ledger
3. Accounts Payable Ledger

A complete chart of accounts and a complete list of all customers and creditors are provided on the inside front cover of Booklet 2.

In the general ledger, all accounts have been opened and the account balances as of April 1, the beginning of a new fiscal period, have been entered. In the accounts receivable ledger and the accounts payable ledger, all accounts have been opened and all amounts due or owed are shown.

MANUAL INSTRUCTIONS

This practice set is designed to be used with the business forms and/or with the Narrative of Transactions, both of which may be found in Booklet 3.

Journalizing Transactions

The business forms are the source of information regarding the transactions and are the basis for the journal entries. Open Booklet 3 and follow the instructions contained in it.

Using the business forms and/or the narrative, begin journalizing the transactions. (*Note:* Post daily to the subsidiary ledgers.)

Posting to the General Ledger

1. Total each column of the various special journals. Ensure that total debits equal total credits in each journal.
2. Post all items that need to be posted individually to the general ledger. The general ledger account balances do not need to be determined until the posting is completed. Use the printed page numbers in your posting references.
3. Post the appropriate totals in the special journals to their respective accounts in the general ledger. Determine the balance of each account. The cash balance on April 30 should be $146,131.01.

Month-End Processing

Since the proprietor, Marty Chavez, considers each month to be a separate fiscal period, you must now complete month-end processing.

Ruled forms are provided for the trial balance, schedules, and financial statements. A work sheet is provided, and its use is optional. The heading, with the exception of the date line, is printed on each form. Also, all general ledger account titles are printed on the work sheet.

1. Prepare schedules of accounts receivable and accounts payable, and compare the totals with the balances of the controlling accounts in the general ledger.
2. Prepare a trial balance at April 30. (Completing the work sheet is optional.)
3. Make necessary adjustments. Record adjusting entries on page 6 of the general journal. Adjustment data are as follows:

a) Merchandise Inventory per physical count, April 30	$208,554.75
b) Office supplies on hand at April 30	1,600.00
c) Store supplies on hand at April 30	3,005.00
d) Prepaid Insurance: Transfer 1/12 of the premium paid on April 2 to expense.	
Depreciation for the month:	
e) Equipment	1,250.00
f) Building	2,475.00
g) Interest earned on note receivable	30.00
h) Accrued salaries at April 30:	
Sales salaries	1,200.00
Office salaries	500.00
Record the estimate of customer returns of this month's sales:	
i) Customer refunds .... (debit Sales, credit Customer Refunds Payable)	4,470.00
j) Returns inventory .... (debit Est. Returns Inventory, credit Cost of Merchandise Sold)	3,190.00

4. Prepare an income statement, a statement of owner's equity, and a balance sheet.
5. Journalize the adjusting entries and post to the general ledger.
6. Journalize the closing entries on page 7 of the general journal. Post to the general ledger, indicating closed accounts by inserting a horizontal line in both balance columns.
7. Prepare a post-closing trial balance.

GENERAL LEDGER SOFTWARE INSTRUCTIONS

Carefully read the introduction and general instructions to the Fit & Fashionable practice set on pages 1–3 of Booklet 1, and review the chart of accounts on the inside cover of Booklet 2. Follow the steps below to complete this practice set using the Cengage Learning General Ledger (CLGL) software inside the *CengageNOW* learning management system.

1. This practice set is broken into three separate assignment parts, each graded separately. When you begin the second and third parts, all account balances will be set correctly for the beginning of that part, in order to prevent any previous errors from compounding.
2. To access additional help with the General Ledger functions, click on the **Help** button that appears near the bottom of the screen. (Note that you may need to scroll down and over to see this button.)
3. All account setups and opening balances required to begin this problem are loaded when you select the problem from the **CengageNOW** assignment menu. Click on the **Save and Exit** button at the bottom of your screen at any point to save your work if you need to stop working to continue later. Your work will automatically be restored when you return.
4. For Parts 1 and 2:
    a. Set the **System Date** near the bottom of the screen to **4/01/16** for Part 1, or **4/16/16** for Part 2. (Note that you may need to scroll down to see the System Date box.)
    b. Enter the journal entries required (if any) from the transactions or source documents dated April 1 through April 15 for Part 1, or those dated April 16 through April 30, up to but not including the Adjusting Entries. Click on the **General Ledger** tab, and then select the appropriate journal entry from the **Tasks** menu in the left menu bar, using the following criteria:
        - Record the purchase of inventory on account only, and any other transactions with credits to Accounts Payable, in the **Purchases Journal**.
        - Record sales of inventory on account only in the **Sales Journal**, using the invoice number as the reference. (Note that this journal is called the Revenue Journal in some texts.)
        - Record ALL cash payments, for whatever reason, in the **Cash Payments Journal**, using the check number as the reference.
        - Record ALL cash receipts, including cash sales, in the **Cash Receipts Journal**.
        - Record adjustments and any other transactions that do not fit the above criteria in the **General Journal**.
        - Detailed instructions for entering transactions in each journal are found in the online instructions attached to each part of the set.

c. Display and review the journal entries. Click on each journal report item under the **Journal Reports** menu on the left menu bar. If you have been asked to print these reports, click on the **Print** button.

d. Make corrections to the journal entries, if necessary. Go to the appropriate journal entry task, click on the entry you wish to correct, then make any corrections to the journal entry, and click on the **Post** button to confirm your changes.

e. Display and review the trial balance, which will be the unadjusted trial balance at the end of Part 2. Click on the **Trial Balance** item under the **Ledger Reports** menu. If you have been asked to print this report, click on the **Print** button.

f. Display and review the schedule of accounts receivable. Click on the **Schedule of Accounts Receivable** item under the **Ledger Reports** menu on the left menu bar. To print the report, click on the **Print** button. Repeat for the schedule of accounts payable.

g. When you are comfortable that you have completed all steps of the problem correctly, click on the **Check My Work** button on the bottom of your screen if it is available, or click on the **Submit Assignment for Grading** button on the lower right of your screen if this is the only item in the assignment. The program will then display the results of the grading, indicating accounts in error with a red **X**. Note that grading in Cengage Learning General Ledger is based on getting each General Ledger account, customer account, and vendor account to its correct ending balance, rather than grading journal transactions individually. This means that the order of transactions in the general journal is not graded, so you may add transactions and also delete or correct transactions without penalty if you run into difficulty with the assignment.

5. For Part 3:

a. Set the **System Date** near the bottom of the screen to **4/30/16**. (Note that you may need to scroll down to see the System Date box.)

b. Display and review the unadjusted trial balance. Click on the **Trial Balance** option under the **Ledger Reports** menu on the left menu bar. To print the report, click on the **Print** button.

c. Enter the adjusting entries noted in step 3 of the Month-End Processing instructions for April 30 (see page 2) in the General Journal. Click on the **General Ledger** tab, and then select **General Journal** from the **Tasks** menu on the left menu bar. Enter journal entries as in the prior parts, but enter **Adj.Ent**. in the **Refer**. column. After each journal entry is entered, click on the **Post** button to post the entry to the General Ledger.

d. Display and review the adjusting entries. Click on the **General Journal** item under the **Journal Reports** menu on the left menu bar. Under **Customize Report** select **Adj.Ent.** from the **Reference** drop-down list to display just the adjusting entries. If you have been asked to print the report, click on the **Print** button.

e. Make corrections to the journal entries, if necessary, using the **General Journal** task, and click on the **Post** button to confirm your changes.

f. Display the adjusted trial balance. Click on the **Trial Balance** item under the **Ledger Reports** menu on the left menu bar. To print the report, click on the **Print** button.

g. Display and review the income statement and statement of owner's equity. Click on the **Income Statement** item and then **Statement of Owner's Equity** item under the **Financial Statements** menu on the left menu bar. To print the report, click on the **Print** button.

h. If you have a **Check My Work** button near the bottom of your screen, click on it to review the grading so far. Your income, expense and capital items will all be incorrect at this point, as you still need to close the income statement accounts. However, your asset and liability accounts should now be correct. If they are not, review the Journal Entry report and the General Ledger report. Make corrections if necessary.

i. Perform period-end closing. Select **Generate Closing Entries** from the **Tasks** menu on the left menu bar. When the dialog box appears, click **Yes** to confirm that you wish the computer to generate the closing journal entries. Review the closing entries for correctness, and then click on the **Post** button to post them to the General Ledger.

j. Display and review the closing journal entries. Click on the **General Journal** item under the **Journals** menu on the left menu bar. Under **Customize Report** select **Clo.Ent.** from the **Reference** drop-down list to display just the closing entries. To print the report, click on the **Print** button.

k. Display and review the balance sheet. Click on the **Balance Sheet** item under the **Financial Statements** menu of the left menu bar to display this statement. To print the report, click on the **Print** button. Make corrections to the journal entries, if necessary.

l. Display the post-closing trial balance. Click on the **Trial Balance** item under the **Ledger Reports** menu of the left menu bar. To print the report, click on the **Print** button.

m. When you are comfortable that you have completed all steps of the problem correctly, click on the **Check My Work** button if it is available, or click on the **Submit Assignment for Grading** button in the lower right of your screen if this is the only item in the assignment.

JOURNALS
AND
RULED FORMS

GENERAL JOURNAL

PAGE 5

	DATE	DESCRIPTION	POST. REF.	DEBIT	CREDIT	
1						1
2						2
3						3
4						4
5						5
6						6
7						7
8						8
9						9
10						10
11						11
12						12
13						13
14						14
15						15
16						16
17						17
18						18
19						19
20						20
21						21
22						22
23						23
24						24
25						25
26						26
27						27
28						28
29						29
30						30
31						31
32						32
33						33

GENERAL JOURNAL

PAGE 6

	DATE	DESCRIPTION	POST. REF.	DEBIT	CREDIT	
1		**Adjusting Entries**				1
2						2
3						3
4						4
5						5
6						6
7						7
8						8
9						9
10						10
11						11
12						12
13						13
14						14
15						15
16						16
17						17
18						18
19						19
20						20
21						21
22						22
23						23
24						24
25						25
26						26
27						27
28						28
29						29
30						30
31						31
32						32
33						33

GENERAL JOURNAL

PAGE 7

	DATE		DESCRIPTION	POST. REF.	DEBIT	CREDIT	
1			**Closing Entries**				1
2							2
3							3
4							4
5							5
6							6
7							7
8							8
9							9
10							10
11							11
12							12
13							13
14							14
15							15
16							16
17							17
18							18
19							19
20							20
21							21
22							22
23							23
24							24
25							25
26							26
27							27
28							28
29							29
30							30
31							31
32							32
33							33

GENERAL JOURNAL

PAGE 8

	DATE	DESCRIPTION	POST. REF.	DEBIT	CREDIT	
1						1
2						2
3						3
4						4
5						5
6						6
7						7
8						8
9						9
10						10
11						11
12						12
13						13
14						14
15						15
16						16
17						17
18						18
19						19
20						20
21						21
22						22
23						23
24						24
25						25
26						26
27						27
28						28
29						29
30						30
31						31
32						32
33						33

REVENUE JOURNAL

PAGE 2

	DATE	INV. NO.	ACCOUNT DEBITED	POST. REF.	ACCTS. REC. DR. SALES CR.	COST OF MERCH. SOLD DR. MERCH. INVENTORY CR.	
1							1
2							2
3							3
4							4
5							5
6							6
7							7
8							8
9							9
10							10
11							11
12							12
13							13
14							14
15							15
16							16
17							17
18							18
19							19
20							20
21							21
22							22
23							23
24							24
25							25
26							26
27							27
28							28
29							29
30							30
31							31
32							32

PURCHASES

	DATE		ACCOUNT CREDITED	POST. REF.	ACCOUNTS PAYABLE CR.	MERCHANDISE INVENTORY DR.	
1							1
2							2
3							3
4							4
5							5
6							6
7							7
8							8
9							9
10							10
11							11
12							12
13							13
14							14
15							15
16							16
17							17
18							18
19							19
20							20
21							21
22							22
23							23
24							24
25							25
26							26

JOURNAL

PAGE 2

	STORE SUPPLIES DR.	OTHER ACCOUNTS DR.			
		ACCOUNT	POST. REF.	AMOUNT	
1					1
2					2
3					3
4					4
5					5
6					6
7					7
8					8
9					9
10					10
11					11
12					12
13					13
14					14
15					15
16					16
17					17
18					18
19					19
20					20
21					21
22					22
23					23
24					24
25					25
26					26

CASH RECEIPTS

	DATE		ACCOUNT CREDITED	POST. REF.	OTHER ACCOUNTS CR.	
1						1
2						2
3						3
4						4
5						5
6						6
7						7
8						8
9						9
10						10
11						11
12						12
13						13
14						14
15						15
16						16
17						17
18						18
19						19
20						20
21						21
22						22
23						23
24						24
25						25

JOURNAL PAGE 2

	MERCH. INV. CR. COST OF MERCH. SOLD DR.	SALES CR.	ACCOUNTS RECEIVABLE CR.	CASH DR.	
1					1
2					2
3					3
4					4
5					5
6					6
7					7
8					8
9					9
10					10
11					11
12					12
13					13
14					14
15					15
16					16
17					17
18					18
19					19
20					20
21					21
22					22
23					23
24					24
25					25

CASH PAYMENTS JOURNAL

PAGE 2

	DATE	CK. NO.	ACCOUNT DEBITED	POST. REF.	OTHER ACCOUNTS DR.	ACCOUNTS PAYABLE DR.	CASH CR.	
1								1
2								2
3								3
4								4
5								5
6								6
7								7
8								8
9								9
10								10
11								11
12								12
13								13
14								14
15								15
16								16
17								17
18								18
19								19
20								20
21								21
22								22
23								23
24								24
25								25
26								26

Fit & Fashionable

Trial Balance

ACCOUNT	DEBIT	CREDIT

Fit & Fashionable

Schedule of Accounts Receivable

Fit & Fashionable

Schedule of Accounts Payable

Fit & Fashionable

Income Statement

Fit & Fashionable
Statement of Owner's Equity

Fit & Fashionable

Balance Sheet

Fit & Fashionable

Balance Sheet (Concluded)

Fit & Fashionable

Post-Closing Trial Balance

ACCOUNT	DEBIT	CREDIT

Fit &

Work

	ACCOUNT TITLE	TRIAL BALANCE DEBIT	TRIAL BALANCE CREDIT	ADJUSTMENTS DEBIT	ADJUSTMENTS CREDIT	
1	*Cash*					1
2	*Notes Receivable*					2
3	*Accounts Receivable*					3
4	*Interest Receivable*					4
5	*Merchandise Inventory*					5
6	*Estimated Returns Inventory*					6
7	*Office Supplies*					7
8	*Store Supplies*					8
9	*Prepaid Insurance*					9
10	*Land*					10
11	*Building*					11
12	*Accum. Deprec.—Building*					12
13	*Equipment*					13
14	*Accum. Deprec.—Equipment*					14
15	*Accounts Payable*					15
16	*Salaries Payable*					16
17	*Customer Refunds Payable*					17
18	*Notes Payable*					18
19	*Marty Chavez, Capital*					19
20	*Marty Chavez, Drawing*					20
21	*Sales*					21
22	*Cost of Merchandise Sold*					22
23	*Sales Salaries Expense*					23
24	*Advertising Expense*					24
25	*Store Supplies Expense*					25
26	*Miscellaneous Selling Expense*					26
27	*Office Salaries Expense*					27
28	*Depr. Expense—Equipment*					28
29	*Insurance Expense*					29
30	*Office Supplies Expense*					30
31	*Depr. Expense—Building*					31
32	*Miscellaneous Admin. Expense*					32
33	*Interest Revenue*					33
34	*Interest Expense*					34
35						35
36						36
37						37
38						38

Fashionable

Sheet

	ADJUSTED TRIAL BALANCE		INCOME STATEMENT		BALANCE SHEET		
	DEBIT	CREDIT	DEBIT	CREDIT	DEBIT	CREDIT	
1							1
2							2
3							3
4							4
5							5
6							6
7							7
8							8
9							9
10							10
11							11
12							12
13							13
14							14
15							15
16							16
17							17
18							18
19							19
20							20
21							21
22							22
23							23
24							24
25							25
26							26
27							27
28							28
29							29
30							30
31							31
32							32
33							33
34							34
35							35
36							36
37							37
38							38